Aberdeenshire

www.raintreepublishers.co.uk
Visit our website to find out
more information about
Raintree books.

To order:
☎ Phone 0845 6044371
🖷 Fax +44 (0) 1865 312263
🖳 Email myorders@raintreepublishers.co.uk

Customers from outside the UK please telephone +44 1865 312262

Raintree is an imprint of
Capstone Global Library Limited, a
company incorporated in England
and Wales having its registered
office at 7 Pilgrim Street, London,
EC4V 6LB - Registered company
number: 6695582

First published by Raintree in 2013
The moral rights of the proprietor have been asserted.

Originally published by DC Comics in the U.S. in single
magazine form as Superman Adventures #3.
Copyright © 2012 DC Comics. All Rights Reserved.

Ashley C. Andersen Zantop *Publisher*
Michael Dahl *Editorial Director*
Donald Lemke & Sean Tulien *Editors*
Heather Kindseth *Creative Director*
Bob Lentz *Designer*
Kathy McColley *Production Specialist*

DC COMICS
Mike McAvennie *Original U.S. Editor*
Bruce Timm *Cover Artist*

ISBN 978 1 406 25401 3
16 15 14 13 12
10 9 8 7 6 5 4 3 2 1
Printed and bound in China by Nordica.
0512/CA21200799
British Library Cataloguing in Publication Data
A full catalogue record for this book is available
from the British Library.

SUPERMAN ADVENTURES

Distant Thunder

Scott McCloud...................... writer
Rick Burchett ....penciller
Terry Austin .... inker
Marie Severin .... colorist
Lois Buhalis...................... letterer

Superman created by
Jerry Siegel & Joe Shuster

IF I WANT TO, I CAN WATCH THE CONFRONTATION BETWEEN *JOR-EL* AND *BRAINIAC*.

FATHER HAD DISCOVERED THAT KRYPTON WAS DOOMED--

--BUT *BRAINIAC*, THE WORLD-WIDE NETWORK OF COMPUTERS THAT WAS SUPPOSED TO *SAFEGUARD* KRYPTON, HAD CONVINCED THE REST OF THE POPULATION THAT JOR-EL WAS *WRONG*.

NOW I'M WATCHING THE TOWERS OF THE CAPITAL CITY BUCKLING AND TOPPLING AS THE PLANET COMES APART.

BRAINIAC KNEW THE TRUTH, BUT HE CHOSE TO SAVE *HIMSELF* INSTEAD BY TRANSMITTING HIS OWN DATA TO AN ORBITING SATELLITE SO AS TO *ESCAPE* THE EXPLODING WORLD...

...JUST AS *I* ESCAPED WHEN MY FATHER SENT ME, AS AN INFANT, TO EARTH ON THAT TINY SPACECRAFT YOU'VE BEEN STUDYING.

THIS IS THE *LAST* WE'LL EVER *SEE* OF KRYPTON. THANKS TO BRAINIAC, THAT LIGHT HAS BEEN PUT OUT *FOREVER*.

ACTUALLY, THAT'S NOT *ENTIRELY* CORRECT.

THERE'S SOMETHING I WANT TO SHOW YOU.

7

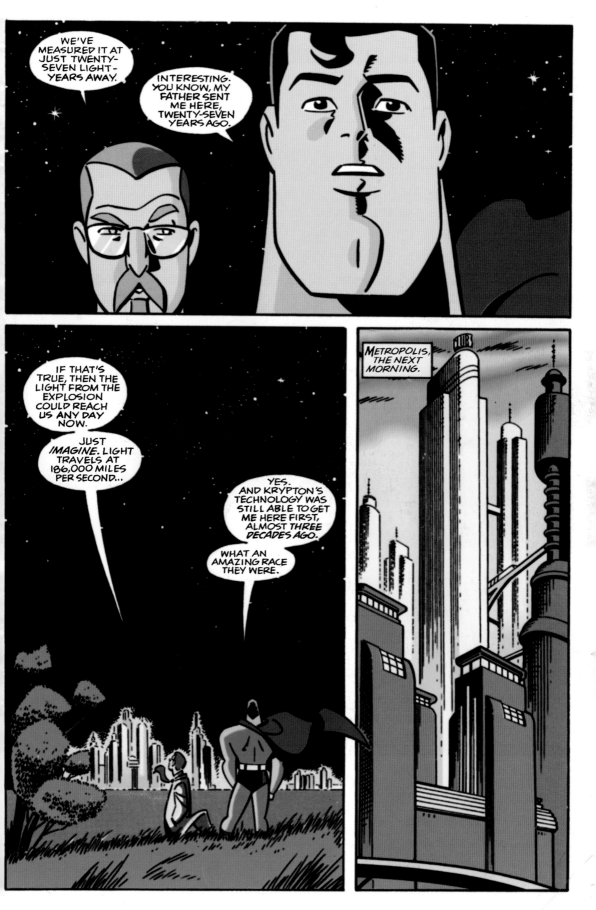

14

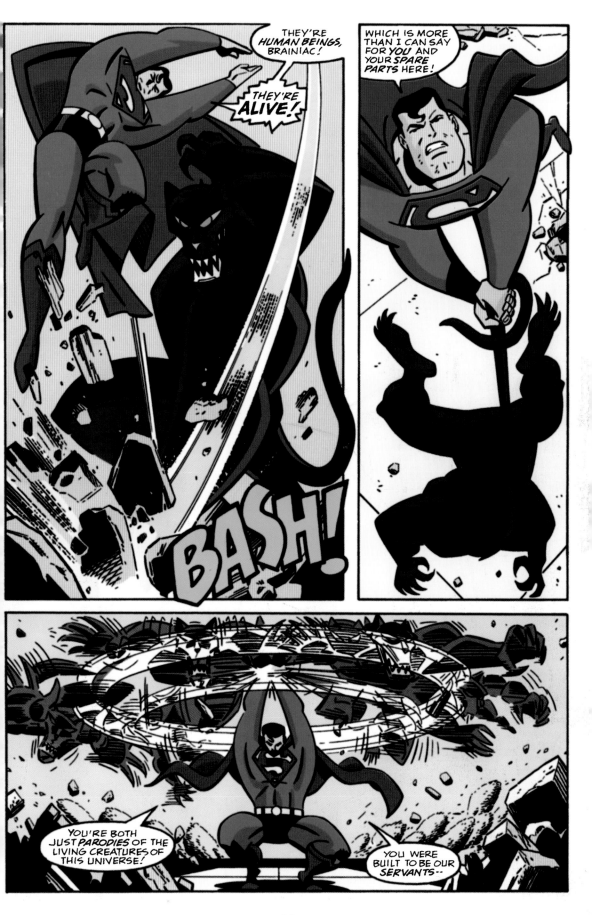

19

SCOTT McCLOUD *WRITER*

Scott McCloud is an acclaimed comics creator and author whose best-known work is the graphic novel *Understanding Comics*. His work also includes the science-fiction adventure series *Zot!*, a 12-issue run of *Superman Adventures*, and much more. Scott is the creator of the "24 Hour Comic," and frequently lectures on comics theory.

RICK BURCHETT *PENCILLER*

Rick Burchett has worked as a comics artist for more than 25 years. He has received the comics industry's Eisner Award three times, Spain's Haxtur Award, and he has been nominated for England's Eagle Award. Rick lives with his wife and two sons in Missouri, USA.

TERRY AUSTIN *INKER*

Throughout his career, inker Terry Austin has received dozens of awards for his work on high-profile comics for DC Comics and Marvel, such as *The Uncanny X-Men, Doctor Strange, Justice League America, Green Lantern,* and *Superman Adventures.* He lives in New York, USA.

GLOSSARY

bluff to say and act like something is true when it isn't in order to trick someone

confrontation open conflict or fight between two or more opposing sides

distressed if someone is distressed, they are worried, or they feel great pain or sadness

facilitate to make something easier

faint not clear or strong

formidable frightening or powerful

leeching clinging to someone or something in hopes of getting something in return

light-year distance traversed by light in one solar year, or about 5.88 trillion miles.

manufacturing making something, often with machines

parodies imitations of something serious that makes fun of or mocks it

pulverize to demolish or crush completely

suspicion thought, based more on feeling than on fact, that something is wrong or bad

SUPERMAN GLOSSARY

Brainiac: an evil, alien robot who destroyed Superman's home planet, Krypton.

Clark Kent: Superman's alter ego, Clark Kent, is a reporter for the *Daily Planet* newspaper and was raised by Ma and Pa Kent. No one knows he is Superman except for his adopted parents, the Kents.

The Daily Planet: the city of Metropolis's biggest and most read newspaper. Clark, Lois, Jimmy, and Perry all work for the *Daily Planet*.

Invulnerability: Superman's invulnerability makes him impervious to harm. Almost nothing can hurt him -- except for Kryptonite, a radioactive rock from his home planet, Krypton.

Krypton: the planet where Superman was born. Brainiac destroyed Krypton shortly after Superman's parents sent him on his way to Earth.

Lois Lane: like Clark Kent, Lois is a reporter at the *Daily Planet* newspaper. She is also one of Clark's best friends.

Metropolis: the city where Clark Kent (Superman) lives.

Professor Hamilton: a brilliant inventor and scientist from S.T.A.R. Labs.

S.T.A.R. Labs: a research center in Metropolis, where scientists make high-tech tools and devices for Superman and other heroes.

VISUAL QUESTIONS & PROMPTS

1 Which character is speaking which line in the panel at right? Explain how you know which balloon belongs to Superman and which belongs to Dr. Hamilton.

2 Why do you think Lois Lane doesn't like the way people are acting while they watch Superman fight Brainiac? Explain your answer using examples from the story.

2 What does Superman mean by calling Brainiac's body a "symbol"? How does that "symbol" relate to the Kryptonian Orb?

HE'S GONE, LOIS. THAT FIGURE YOU SEE IS JUST A HARMLESS STATUE NOW.

A SYMBOL.

3

4 In the panel at right, why do you think Brainiac says what he says to Superman? Why does he want Superman to think people are beneath him?

Ooh, GOOD ONE!

LISTEN TO THEM PRATTLE ON, KAL-EL. IS *THIS* THE RACE OF WITLESS PRIMITIVES YOU'VE SWORN TO PROTECT?

THEY ARE *BENEATH* YOU.

4

5 Why do you think Brainiac split up his black cat robots into single cats at first? What advantages do you think it gave him? Why did he merge them into a single, bigger cat robot when Superman intervened?

THEY'RE GATHERING! IT'S LIKE THEY'RE ALL BEING CONTROLLED FROM A SINGLE MIND!

5

WHA
W
HE

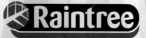